BRAIN ACADEMY
SUPERMATHS

Louise Moore, Pete Crawford
and Richard Cooper

Mission File 3

Years 4-5

roduced in association with

National Association
for Able Children
in Education

RISING STARS

Rising Stars are grateful to the following people for their support in developing this series: Sue Mordecai, Julie Fitzpatrick, Johanna Raffan, Belle Wallace and Clive Tunnicliffe.

NACE, PO Box 242, Arnolds Way, Oxford OX2 9FR
www.nace.co.uk

Rising Stars UK Ltd, 22 Grafton Street, London W1S 4EX
www.risingstars-uk.com

Published 2007
Text, design and layout © Rising Stars UK Ltd.

Editorial Consultant: Jean Carnall
Cover design: Burville-Riley
Design: Pentacor**big**
Illustrations: Cover – Burville-Riley / Characters – Bill Greenhead

British Library Cataloguing in Publication Data.
A CIP record for this book is available from the British Library.

ISBN: 978-1-84680-232-4

Printed by Craft Print International Ltd, Singapore

CONTENTS

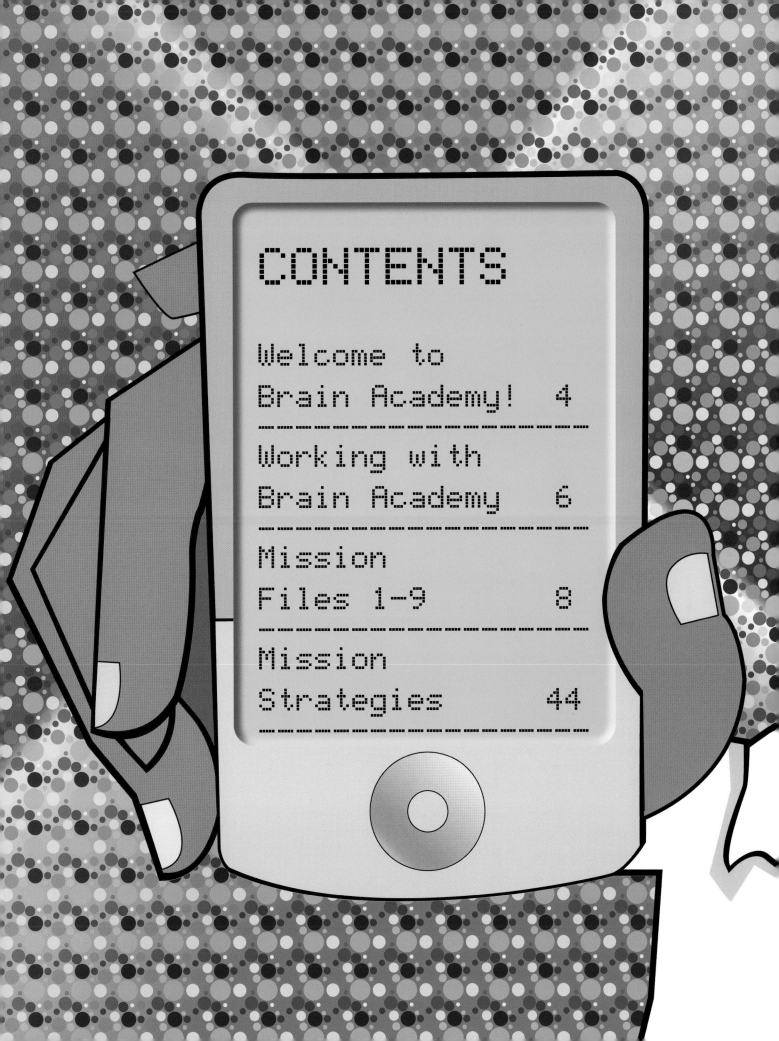

Welcome to Brain Academy!

Welcome to Brain Academy! Make yourself at home. We are here to give you the low-down on the organisation – so pay attention!

It's our job to help Da Vinci and his colleagues to solve the tough problems they face and we would like you to join us as members of the Academy. Are you up to the challenge?

Da Vinci
Da Vinci is the founder and head of the Brain Academy. He is all seeing, all thinking and all knowing – possibly the cleverest person alive. Nobody has ever actually seen him in the flesh as he communicates only via computer. When Da Vinci receives an emergency call for help, the members of Brain Academy jump into action (and that means you!).

Huxley
Huxley is Da Vinci's right-hand man. Not as clever, but still very smart. He is here to guide you through the missions and offer help and advice. The sensible and reliable face of Brain Academy, Huxley is cool under pressure.

Dr Hood
The mad doctor is the arch-enemy of Da Vinci and Brain Academy. He has set up a rival organisation called D.A.F.T. (which stands for Dull And Feeble Thinkers). Dr Hood and his agents will do anything they can to irritate and annoy the good people of this planet. He is a pain we could do without.

Hilary Kumar
Ms Kumar is the Prime Minister of our country. As the national leader she has a hotline through to the Academy but will only call in an extreme emergency. Confident and strong willed, she is a very tough cookie indeed.

General Cods-Wallop
This highly decorated gentleman (with medals, not wallpaper) is in charge of the armed forces. Most of his success has come from the help of Da Vinci and the Academy rather than the use of his somewhat limited military brain.

Mrs Tiggles
Stella Tiggles is the retired head of the Secret Intelligence service. She is a particular favourite of Da Vinci who treats her as his own mother. Mrs Tiggles' faithful companion is her cat, Bond... James Bond.

We were just like you once – ordinary schoolchildren leading ordinary lives. Then one day we all received a call from a strange character named Da Vinci. From that day on, we have led a double life – as secret members of Brain Academy!

Here are a few things you should know about the people you'll meet on your journey.

Inspector Pattern
The trusty Inspector is Buster's right-hand lady. Ms Pattern looks for clues in data and is the complete opposite to the muddled D.A.F.T. agents. Using her mathematical mind to find order where there is chaos, she is a welcome addition to Da Vinci's team. In fact some of the team would do well to think in such a methodical way… a certain Mr Blastov perhaps?

Maryland T. Wordsworth
M.T. Wordsworth is the president of the USA. Not the sharpest tool in the box, Maryland prefers to be known by his middle name, Texas, or 'Tex' for short. He takes great exception to being referred to as 'Mary' (which has happened in the past).

Buster Crimes
Buster is a really smooth dude and is in charge of the Police Force. His laid-back but efficient style has won him many friends, although these don't include Dr Hood or the agents of D.A.F.T. who regularly try to trick the coolest cop in town.

Sandy Buckett
The fearless Sandy Buckett is the head of the fire service. Sandy and her team of brave firefighters are always on hand, whether to extinguish the flames of chaos caused by the demented Dr Hood or just to rescue Mrs Tiggles' cat…

Echo the Eco-Warrior
Echo is the hippest chick around. Her love of nature and desire for justice will see her do anything to help an environmental cause – even if it means she's going to get her clothes dirty.

Prince Barrington
Prince Barrington, or 'Bazza' as he is known to his friends, is the publicity-seeking heir to the throne. Always game for a laugh, the Prince will stop at nothing to raise money for worthy causes. A 'good egg' as his mother might say.

Victor Blastov
Victor Blastov is the leading scientist at the Space Agency. He once tried to build a rocket by himself but failed to get the lid off the glue. Victor often requires the services of the Academy, even if it's to set the video to record Dr Who.

Working with Brain Academy

Do you get the idea? Now you've had the introduction we are going to show you the best way to use this book.

Safe and sound

Time: Early afternoon
Place: NASA headquarters

Dr Hood and his D.A.F.T. organisation are up to no good. Well, there's a surprise! They are trying to steal the secret formula for Victor Blastov's rocket fuel. Buster Crimes agrees to help Victor choose a safe to keep the formula from the D.A.F.T. agents' clutches.

This is no open or shut case, Da Vinci. How do I stop those dudes from stealing the formula?

Huxley has a Training Mission for you, Buster. Get cracking!

TM

The local shop has 2 models of safe – the Double-3 and the 3-Switch.

The Double-3 safe has 2 knobs. Each knob has 3 possible settings. This safe is set to the number 31.

1) How many different 2-digit numbers can be set on this safe?

TM

The 3-Switch safe has 3 knobs but each knob only has 2 possible settings.

2) How many different 3-digit numbers can be set on this safe?

3) Do you think Buster should choose the Double-3 or the 3-Switch safe?

Why do you think that?

MM

A shop in town has a larger range of safes. They have the Double-2, Double-3 and Double-4 safes in stock.

1) Find out how many different combinations can be set on each of the safes.
You can use your results from the Training Mission for the Double-3 safe.

8

9

Each mission is divided up into different parts.

The plot

This tells you what the mission is about.

The Training Mission

Huxley will give you some practice before sending you on the main mission.

Each book contains a number of 'missions' for you to take part in. You will work with the characters in Brain Academy to complete these missions.

Huxley's Think Tank

Huxley will give you some useful tips to help you on each mission.

The Main Mission

This is where you try to complete the challenge.

MM 2) Copy this table and fill in the results for the 3 safes that you have worked out.

Safe	Double-1	Double-2	Double-3	Double-4	Double-5
Number of knobs		2	2	2	
Number of settings		2	3	4	
Number of combinations					

Do you notice any pattern in the results?

3) See if you can predict the number of combinations for the Double-5 safe.

HUXLEY'S THINK TANK

- If you need more numbers in a pattern, it can sometimes be easier to work out smaller examples rather than larger ones. For example, it is easier to work out the combinations for the Double-1 safe than the Double-5 safe.

They also have the 2-Switch, 3-Switch and 4-Switch safes in stock.

10

MM 4) Find out how many different combinations can be set on each of the safes. You can use your results from earlier for the Double-2 and 3-Switch safes.

5) Copy this table and fill in the results for the 3 safes that you have worked out.

Safe	1-Switch	2-Switch	3-Switch	4-Switch	5-Switch
Number of knobs		2	3	4	
Number of settings		2	2	2	
Number of combinations					

6) Predict the number of combinations for the 5-Switch safe. It might help to work out the number of combinations for the 1-Switch first.

Safe as houses, man! That rocket fuel formula (and my secret stash of sweets) ain't goin' nowhere.

Do you notice any patterns in the numbers this time?

Da Vinci files

The shopkeeper said that he could also make special orders for the following safes from the Double and Switch range of safes.

- A safe with 36 possible combinations.
- A safe with 128 possible combinations.

Which safes are these – how many knobs and settings do they have?

11

No one said this was easy. In fact, that is why you have been chosen. Da Vinci will only take the best and he believes that includes you. Good luck!

PS: See pages 44–47 for some hints and tips and a useful process.

The Da Vinci Files

These problems are for the best Brain Academy recruits. Very tough. Are you tough enough?

7

Safe and sound

Time: Early afternoon
Place: NASA headquarters

Dr Hood and his D.A.F.T. organisation are up to no good. Well, there's a surprise! They are trying to steal the secret formula for Victor Blastov's rocket fuel. Buster Crimes agrees to help Victor choose a safe to keep the formula from the D.A.F.T. agents' clutches.

> This is no open or shut case, Da Vinci. How do I stop those dudes from stealing the formula?

> Huxley has a Training Mission for you, Buster. Get cracking!

TM

> The local shop has 2 models of safe – the Double-3 and the 3-Switch.

The Double-3 safe has 2 knobs. Each knob has 3 possible settings. This safe is set to the number 31.

1) How many different 2-digit numbers can be set on this safe?

The 3-Switch safe has 3 knobs but each knob only has 2 possible settings.

2) How many different 3-digit numbers can be set on this safe?

3) Do you think Buster should choose the Double-3 or the 3-Switch safe?

Why do you think that?

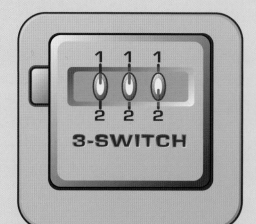

3-SWITCH

MM

A shop in town has a larger range of safes. They have the Double-2, Double-3 and Double-4 safes in stock.

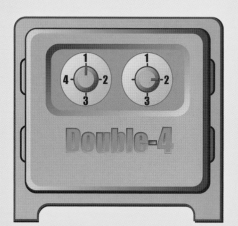

1) Find out how many different combinations can be set on each of the safes.

You can use your results from the Training Mission for the Double-3 safe.

2) Copy this table and fill in the results for the 3 safes that you have worked out.

Safe	Double-1	Double-2	Double-3	Double-4	Double-5
Number of knobs		2	2	2	
Number of settings		2	3	4	
Number of combinations					

Do you notice any pattern in the results?

3) See if you can predict the number of combinations for the Double-5 safe.

HUXLEY'S THINK TANK

- If you need more numbers in a pattern, it can sometimes be easier to work out smaller examples rather than larger ones. For example, it is easier to work out the combinations for the Double-1 safe than the Double-5 safe.

They also have the 2-Switch, 3-Switch and 4-Switch safes in stock.

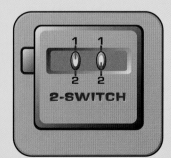

2-SWITCH

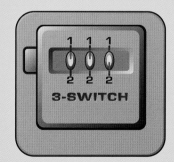

3-SWITCH

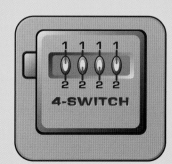

4-SWITCH

MM 4) Find out how many different combinations can be set on each of the safes. You can use your results from earlier for the 3-Switch safe.

5) Copy this table and fill in the results for the 3 safes that you have worked out.

Safe	1-Switch	2-Switch	3-Switch	4-Switch	5-Switch
Number of knobs		2	3	4	
Number of settings		2	2	2	
Number of combinations					

6) Predict the number of combinations for the 5-Switch safe. It might help to work out the number of combinations for the 1-Switch first.

Safe as houses, man! That rocket fuel formula (and my secret stash of sweets) ain't goin' nowhere.

Do you notice any patterns in the numbers this time?

Da Vinci files

The shopkeeper said that he could also make special orders for the following safes from the Double and Switch range of safes.

- A safe with 36 possible combinations.
- A safe with 128 possible combinations.

Which safes are these – how many knobs and settings do they have?

Victor's block-shocker

Time: Is short
Place: Victor's lab

Victor Blastov has some highly reactive blocks. Sometimes, he needs them arranged with the biggest possible length around the edges to stop the blocks producing a huge chemical reaction. Other times, he needs a shorter length around the edges, to increase the chemical reaction.

Argggh! It takes me so long to sort out ze size I need. I keep losing ze new chemicals zat are made, or making zem too soon. Help!

There'll be no errors with the areas once this case is solved.

Blastov needs your help with these shapes or he's going to blow up the lab!

A

B

C

D

E

F

1) Which shapes have the same perimeter? Do they have the same area as well?

2) Which shapes have the same area?
Do they have the same perimeter as well?

HUXLEY'S THINK TANK

- To find the area of a rectangle, multiply the length by the width.
- To find the perimeter of a rectangle, double the sum of the length and the width.

3) 'L' is the length of the rectangle and 'W' is the width.

W

L

a) Find all the possible values of 'L' and 'W' when the area is 20 cm².

b) If the length is 6 cm and the area is less than 50 cm², what could the width be?

Quick, I need to understand ze measurements before ze reactions start again!

Use squared paper.

1) Find all the areas from 1 cm² to 30 cm² that will only make 1 rectangle.

a) Complete the table to show your results.

Area	Only possible rectangle
2	
3	

b) What is the same about all the rectangles in the table?

c) Find the next 2 prime numbers.

HUXLEY'S THINK TANK

- These areas are the group of numbers called PRIME NUMBERS.
- PRIME NUMBERS have exactly 2 factors. The factors are 1 and the number itself. For example, 1 x 5 = 5. There is no other way to make 5, so 5 is a prime number.
- Remember that factors are always whole numbers.

2) a) Which areas between 1 cm² and 30 cm² can you use to make squares.

b) Why are they called square numbers?

3) With an area of 12 cm² you can make 3 different rectangles.

HUXLEY'S THINK TANK

- The sides of the rectangles show the FACTORS of 12. These are 1, 2, 3, 4, 6 and 12.

Find 4 other areas between 1 cm² and 30 cm² that will make just 3 rectangles. Write the areas, then list the factors that each has.

Thanks for all your help. I vos beginning to lose ze plot!

No change there then Victor, old chap.

HUXLEY'S THINK TANK

- You make SQUARE NUMBERS by multiplying a number by itself. 2 x 4 = 4

Da Vinci files

- Find all the numbers less than 30 that have 3 factors. What do you notice about all these numbers?

- Find all the numbers less than 30 that have 4 factors.

- Find all the numbers less than 50 that have 8 factors.

On yer bike!

Time: Curtain up
Place: The circus ring

Prince Barrington has finally persuaded his old school chum, Bertie Bright, to bring his cycling circus to Barrington Hall for the summer. But Bertie's limousine has broken down on his way to the first show and no one else knows how to put the bikes together... Can Bazza save the show?

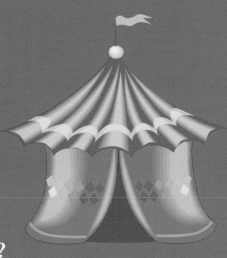

We've got a 'wheel' problem here, Da Vinci. The riders and bikes need sorting out.

We'll soon have this show on the road

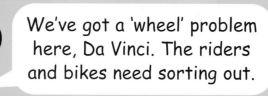

The circus owns unicycles and bicycles.

1) If there are 4 unicycles and 3 bicycles, how many wheels are there?

2) If there are 8 wheels, there could be no bicycles and 8 unicycles. What other options are there?

3) What if there are 13 wheels? Give all the possible answers.

4) If there are 4 riders, give all the possible number of wheels. For example, if each rider is on a unicycle, there will be 4 wheels.

5) If there are 6 cycles, give all the possible number of wheels.

> Well I have 5 riders and 9 wheels here. Spiffing!

What types of cycles has Prince Barrington got?

The circus has bicycles, unicycles and tricycles – these are cycles for 2 riders with 3 wheels.

1) A team uses at least 1 of each type of cycle. There must be 1 person on each unicycle and bicycle. There must be 2 people on each tricycle.

a) If there are 8 people in the team, list all the possible combinations of cycle they could use. For example, they could use 3 tricycles, 1 bicycle and 1 unicycle.

b) What is the maximum number of wheels for 8 riders? What is the minimum number of wheels for 8 riders?

2) a) Work out all the combinations for a team of 7 people.

b) What is the maximum and minimum number of wheels for 7 riders?

3) Work out the maximum and minimum number of wheels for a team of:

a) 6 people   b) 5 people   c) 4 people

MM Copy this table and use your answers to complete it.

Number in the team	Maximum number of wheels	Minimum number of wheels
4	6	6
5		
6		
7		
8		

Describe any patterns you can see.

4) Use your results to work out the maximum and minimum number of wheels for a team of 15 riders.

My gran-mama (Lady Barrington-Farthing) started cycling when she was 95 years old. She's been doing 12 miles a day. I haven't a clue where she is!

Da Vinci files

- Bertie's finally arrived and wants to use the quad bikes with the tricycles, bicycles and unicycles. A quad bike has 4 wheels and 1 rider.

- Starting with a team of 5 riders and working up to a team of 8 riders, work out the maximum and minimum number of wheels for each team.

Explain any patterns in your results. You might be able to make a rule using the patterns you have found!

Make the connection

Time: To refit the computers
Place: Deep inside Brain Academy

A new computer system is being installed and the offices are being rewired. A top security network is being set up.

The network can only be accessed where special rods cross each other. Different levels of access are available depending on the number of rods at each intersection. The more rods there are, the higher the level of access. Most people will need a 2-rod intersection.

Intersection

The rods are extremely expensive. We must make sure we make exactly the right number and type of connections for each office.

I think I can find the connection. My team will sort this out. Huxley, lead the way!

Let's check we can spot the connections first. All these connections are where 2 rods intersect.

 TM

1) Count the number of rods and connections in these examples.

a)

b)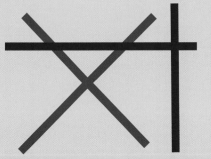

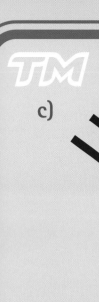

c)

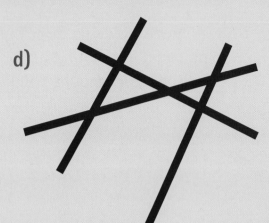

d)

e)

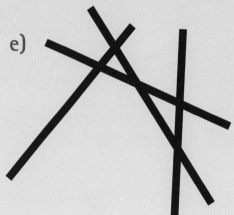

f)

g)

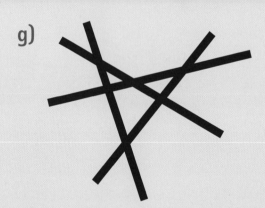

h)

2) Now show us how to make these connections.
Remember, 2 rods must cross at every intersection.

a) Use 4 rods.
Make 4 connections.

b) Use 5 rods.
Make 8 connections.

c) Use 6 rods.
Make 10 connections.

d) Use 4 rods.
Make 5 connections.

e) Use 7 rods.
Make 10 connections.

f) Use 6 rods.
Make 12 connections.

I have a saying about computers – 'machines should work, people should think'.

Indeed. Just get on with it, boy!

1) You have 2 rods. Show all the possible connections that can be made.

2) Show all the possible connections that can be made for

a) 3 rods   b) 4 rods   c) 5 rods

Make a table to show your results.

Do you think you have found all the solutions? Explain why or why not.

3) Use your answers from question 1 to work out the maximum number of connections that can be made from each set of rods. Can you find a pattern in your results?

a) When you have found the pattern, explain how it works.

b) What is this pattern called?

c) Use the pattern from your results to work out how many connections you could make with 8 rods.

d) The publicity office needs 50 connections. Use the pattern to work out the minimum number of rods they need.

e) The code breakers' office needs 160 connections. What is the minimum number of rods they need?

> Da Vinci has got millions of connections. I wonder how many rods he's got?!

Da Vinci files

- To get full access to the top security network you need an intersection of 5 rods.

  Da Vinci's office needs 3 intersections that have full access to the top security network.

  Investigate how many rods are needed to make 3 intersections of 5 rods.

- Huxley's office needs 1 intersection of 5 rods, 2 intersections of 3 rods and 6 intersections of 2 rods.

  Investigate how this could be achieved. Make sure there are no extra connections.

what's going on?

Time: To think logically
Place: Somewhere quiet

Da Vinci is keen to keep the team's problem-solving skills up to scratch so he's come up with some mind-boggling questions to keep their thinking gear in order.

$$3x + 2 = 8$$
$$34 - 7 =$$
$$1 \quad 2^{56} \quad 778$$

> Huxley, it's time to get the team in tip-top condition again. The PM could call on us at any time!

> Yes, sir! I'll round them up and get them going!

TM

> The information needed is given in each question, but it isn't easy to match the right person with the right piece of information. Can you work out who is who?

1) The first group of agents are Katy, Lisa and Sally. Use the information to sort out what colour each person is wearing.

- One person is wearing red.
- Lisa is wearing blue.
- The person wearing green has an 's' in her name.

HUXLEY THINK TANK

- You could make a list of all the possible choices before you start. As you read the information, cross out the things that can't be true and circle the ones that must be true.
- You could also try drawing up two-way tables or Carroll diagrams.

2) The second group of agents are John, David and Clare. You have to work out which agent is carrying which piece of equipment.

- One agent has a walkie-talkie.
- The female agent does not have a hidden spy camera.
- John has a miniature recording machine.

3) The third group of agents are Tom, Ann and Liz. They all visited between Monday and Wednesday. Work out who came when and how they travelled.

- Tom came by aeroplane, but not on Wednesday.
- Liz didn't come on Monday.
- The person travelling by train came on Monday.

1) Buster Crimes needs to sort out the eye colour, hair colour and hair length for Paul, John and Mary.

- Someone has green eyes.
- Paul has blue eyes.
- One person has brown hair.
- John's hair is long but not black.
- Only one person has short hair.
- Mary isn't the person with brown eyes.
- The blonde hair is short.
- Mary has black hair.

2) Three people bought different ice creams from the van. Work out who had which flavour ice cream, what they had on the ice cream and at what time.

- Prince Barrington had an ice cream at 2 p.m., but not chocolate ice cream.
- Huxley had a flake in his ice cream but waited till after dinner to buy it.
- The fruit sauce went with the vanilla ice cream.
- Sandy Bucket had strawberry ice cream.
- Somebody had toffee sauce on their ice cream at 10 a.m.

3) Rewrite the ice cream problem for choices of pizza, chicken or pasta with chips, salad or baked potato for dinner, tea or supper.

These are real Brain Academy 'specials'.

Da Vinci files

Here's the solution to one logic puzzle.

Type of transport	Car	Bike	Bus
Who owns it	John	Andy	Emma
Colour	green	red	blue

- Make your own logic puzzle by writing clues to help people work out the answer.

  Try not to give too much information.

- Use some 'not' statements. Remember that a bike only has two wheels and might not have a motor.

- When you have written the clues, check that you can solve the puzzle with them!

  Test your puzzle on a friend.

- Try making up some more puzzles.

The data is later

Time: Just before
a staff meeting
Place: Huxley's office

The Brain Academy has been involved in an intergalactic mission to improve relationships with the inhabitants of other planets. Da Vinci wants accurate records of what the team did and who they met. It's proving difficult to sort out the details.

I need all the facts and figures in an hour.

Venn and Carroll diagrams could help.

Venn diagrams help, what? And who is zis Carol?

First we need to sort out some information about the agents for Da Vinci.

1) This Venn diagram shows the number of agents from Team X who were on Missions A and B.

Mission A		Mission B	
3	2	1	1

a) How many agents were on Mission A?

b) How many were on Mission B?

c) How many were on both missions?

d) How many were not on either mission?

2) 10 agents were on site.

How many are not men
and not in the canteen?

- 5 were men
- 7 were in the canteen
- 4 men were in the canteen

3) Use the information to fill in the Carroll Diagram.

Of the 10 agents, 5 arrive by car.

Altogether, 4 are late.

4 of the agents who don't
arrive by car are not late.

	Car	Not car
Late		
Not late		

4) 24 of the agents who went on this mission have been on
a similar mission before.

30 can communicate with at least 1 type of alien and 13
of those have not been on a similar mission before.

There were 43 agents on the mission.

a) How many agents had been on a similar mission and could
communicate with aliens?

b) How many agents had been on a similar mission and could not
communicate with aliens?

c) How many agents had not been on a similar mission and could
communicate with aliens?

d) How many agents had not been on a similar mission and could
not communicate with aliens?

The next section of information is about the transport and the visitors.

1) 15 visitors arrive.

> • 8 of them are aliens
> • 3 of the aliens are old
> • 2 are old people

How many of those who are not old are not aliens?

2) 12 aliens stay in the spaceship.

> • 8 of the aliens are green
> • 6 of the aliens have 3 arms
> • 3 of the aliens aren't green and don't have 3 arms

How many of the aliens are green with 3 arms?

3) Try sorting out this alien data about another group of visitors. Some speak Flibos, some are VIPs and some have travelled 5 light years to attend the meeting.

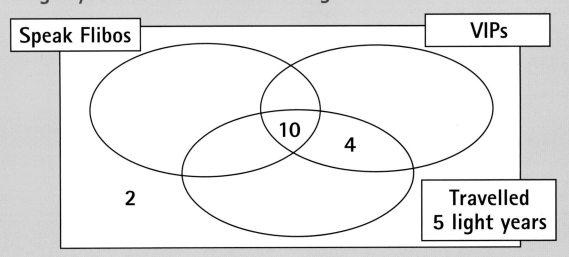

a) Describe what the numbers in the Venn diagram show.

MM

b) Complete the diagram using this information. It's really mixed up!

- 19 visitors speak Flibos.
- Of the vistors who didn't travel 5 light years, there are 3 times as many VIPs who don't speak Flibos as those who do.
- There are 22 VIPs.
- 3 of the Flibos speakers aren't VIPs and travelled 5 light years.
- There are 24 visitors who travelled 5 light years.

Victor thought a spreadsheet was something you put on the bed and that software was a woolly hat!

Da Vinci Files

- 5 spaceships are cone shaped and 6 have wings.
  All the spaceships are either cone shaped or have wings or both.
  How many spaceships are there?
  Find all the possible solutions to this problem.

- Try with 8 cone-shaped spaceships, 3 with wings and 0 with neither.
  What is the possible number of solutions?

- Investigate different numbers of spaceships that are cone shaped, have wings or both but keep the number with neither as 0.

  You could use a table to record your results.

Any patterns in the results?

When is a Gruffle not a Gruffle?

Time: 04:52:31 (roughly)
Place: Victor's lab

Victor has knocked over a box of radioactive shapes while trying to reach his lego set on the top shelf.

Now I understand why Victor's hair glows in the dark... Huxley!

Doh! Before I make ze next plastic brick masterpiece, I need to sort zeez dodgy shapes into ze correct boxes.

Here are the shapes that Victor needs to sort.

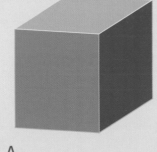

A

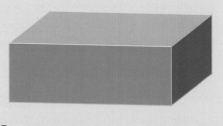

B

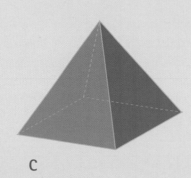

C

D

1) To begin with, Victor thinks that all the shapes with at least one triangular face might belong together.

   Which shapes are these?

2) When he does get those shapes together, they start fizzing, so he separates them again quickly! He then thinks it must be the shapes that have 8 vertices that belong together.

   Which are they?

Vertices are the 'corners' or 'points' of the shape.

3) When those shapes are put together they start reacting too, so once more he separates them. He then thinks it must be the shapes that have an even number of edges that belong together.

   Which are they?

4) Yet again, he was wrong! Suggest another way of sorting the shapes so that a different group is made.

Zis sorting business has reminded me about zeez samples I collected from a previous mission...

Here are the specimens that Victor has collected from the planet Gruff.
He has started sorting them:

All of these are Gruffles.

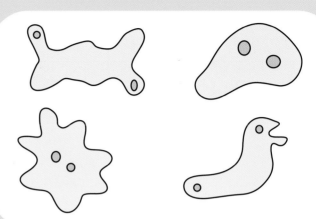

None of these is a Gruffle.

1) Which of these are Gruffles?

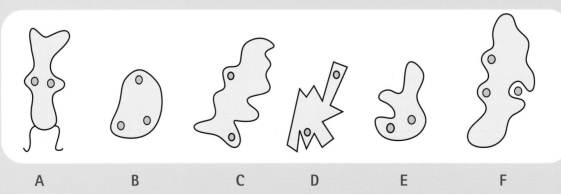

A   B   C   D   E   F

2) Draw your own Gruffle. Make sure it really is a Gruffle!

 Here are the specimens that Victor has collected from the planet Glimp. Once again, he has started sorting them:

All of these are Glimpians.

None of these is a Glimpian.

3) Which of these are Glimpians?

A   B   C   D   E

4) Draw TWO of your own Glimpians. Make sure that both of them really are Glimpians.

Better put ze lego away. Mind I don't trip over zis Gruffle and knock over ze... argghh! (Crash!!!)

Da Vinci files

- Invent a set of creatures called Glogs. Decide what a Glog has to have to be a Glog and draw at least 6 creatures that are Glogs.

- Now draw 6 more creatures that are NOT Glogs. Try to make them as much like Glogs as you can without them actually being Glogs! Challenge a friend to work out what makes a Glog a Glog!

Bazza takes stock...

Time: Product launch
Place: The royal farm

Prince Barrington has decided to market chicken stock cubes to complement the free-range chickens that he has on his organic farm. He has got a production line sorted out but he needs your help to decide how to package them.

My stock cubes will be the finest in the shops! But I'm not counting my chickens until I've sorted out this packaging lark. Any ideas, Da Vinci?

I think we might have an eggs-planation... take it away, Huxley!

Prince Barrington wants to sell 3 different-sized boxes of Chixo cubes. Can you help him?

The small box will hold 8 cubes. He found that there are lots of ways of arranging 8 cubes so they fill a box. Here are some of them.

The medium box will hold 12 cubes.

1) How can the 12 cubes be arranged so that they fill a box?
   Find as many different ways as you can and record them.

HUXLEY'S THINK TANK

- It might help to think about layers. What number of cubes can be used in 1 layer if all the layers are going to use 12 cubes?

- You could always get 12 cubes to help you. Whenever you find a different way of filling the box, count the number of cubes you have in each layer. You might notice something about those numbers and the fact that there are 12 cubes altogether.

Wonder why I'm interested in chickens? I had an uncle who thought he was a chicken. My aunt nearly left him – but we needed the eggs!

1) The large box will hold 18 cubes. Find as many different ways as you can of arranging the 18 cubes so they fill a box. Record all the ways you find.

Small – 8 cubes

2) Which box would you choose to pack the 18 cubes? Why would you choose it?

3) Are there any arrangements of 18 cubes that you think would NOT be very good for boxes? Why do you think that?

Medium – 12 cubes

4) Prince Barrington's cooks are preparing for a royal banquet.

Some cooks are making chicken stew. They need 72 cubes altogether. How many small boxes do they need to have exactly 72 cubes?

Large – 18 cubes

Can they use:

a) just medium boxes?

b) just large boxes?

c) a mixture of small and medium boxes?

d) a mixture of medium and large boxes?

e) a mixture of small, medium and large boxes?

5) Some other cooks are making chicken soup. They only have medium and large boxes of Chixo cubes and they need 100 Chixo cubes altogether. Can they use:

a) just medium boxes?

b) just large boxes?

c) a mixture of medium and large boxes?

What mixture of medium and large boxes should they use to get the 100 cubes with the smallest number of cubes left over?

What is the smallest number of boxes they can use to get the 100 cubes that they need?

Is there more than 1 way of doing this?

Medium – 12 cubes

Large – 18 cubes

Da Vinci files

This is Prince Barrington's favourite arrangement for the small box.

He likes it because the box is a cube.

He likes it so much that he decides that all the boxes should be cubes.

- 8 Chixo cubes fill the smallest box. How many will there be in the next 2 sizes of boxes that are cubes?

- Prince Barrington wants to make a giant box for his kitchens. The box must hold at least 500 Chixo cubes and it must be a cube shape. What is the smallest number of cubes it can contain?

Cycle paths

Time: To get on your bike
Place: Echo's ecological pavilion

Echo is planning a sponsored bike ride to raise money for her new eco project – 'green bridges' over busy roads in her local towns. The bridges will be planted with trees and grass and create safe links for cyclists and pedestrians. To raise enough money, she wants the bike ride to use as many of the local roads as possible.

A sponsored bike ride is just the ticket to raise money for our 'green bridges' project! I have to make sure that it gets maximum publicity so that our bridges can be planted with gorgeous trees and flowers and bushes and...

We get the picture, Echo! It's a 'wheely' great idea but have you thought about which routes you want the cyclists to take?

Er, no, I hadn't really given that part of the plan much attention...

Hmmm. Just as well the BA team are here to help then. Lead the way, Huxley!

I hope Echo knows how far she has to go...

TM

Look at these possible routes for the sponsored bike ride.

Find the routes where you can travel along all the roads without using any road more than once.

You can visit the same town more than once if you want to.

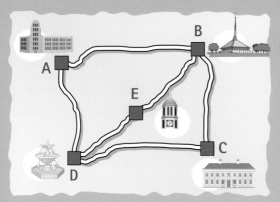

Route 1

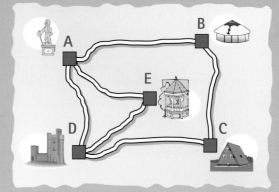

Route 2

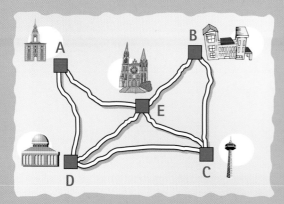

Route 3

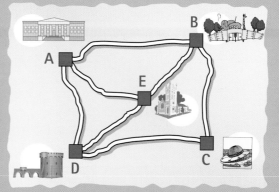

Route 4

HUXLEY'S THINK TANK

- Try drawing the routes without lifting your pencil off the paper or going over any road twice. If you get stuck, starting at a different town might help you!

MM

1) Try these routes. For each route, find out whether you can or cannot travel along all the roads without using any road more than once.

a)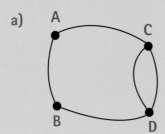

b)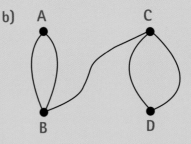

c)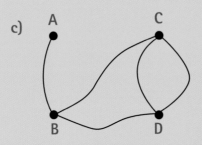

d)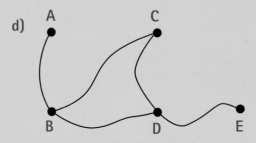

2) Echo found that, as long as she started at Town A, she could cycle along every road in this route:

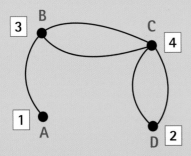

She noticed that each town had a different number of roads.

Town A had just 1 road, Town B had 3 roads, Town C had 4 roads and Town D had 2.

She labelled each town with its number of roads.

Copy the routes from question 1 and count the number of roads at each town. Label the towns with these numbers.

3) Look at the routes where you could travel along each road just once. For each of these routes, how many towns have an odd number of roads?

4) Look at the routes where you could NOT travel along each road just once. For each of these routes, how many towns have an odd number of roads?

5) When you can travel along each road just once, do you start at a town with an odd number of roads or an even number? Where do you finish?

Gasp, I'm exhausted. Even my bike can't stand up.

Indeed, my dear – that's because it's 'two-tyred'!

Da Vinci files

Look at this map. What is the largest number of roads you can travel along without using any road twice?

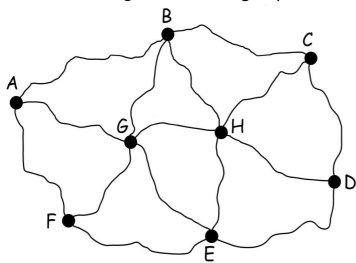

Mission Strategies

MISSION FILE 3:1

If you are having trouble in the Training Mission working out how many different numbers can be set on the safes, try listing all the different combinations. Look out for repeats!

In the Main Mission, when you are looking for patterns in sequences of numbers, it can often be quite helpful to look at the differences between each of the numbers in the sequence.

MISSION FILE 3:2

When you draw rectangles, use squared paper and make sure the sides of the shapes are on the lines on the paper. This makes it easy to work out the areas. Test for different areas by starting with a rectangle of width 1 cm, then 2 cm, 3 cm and so on to see which work. When you are looking for factors, remember they must be whole numbers. Drawing rectangles will help you with the Da Vinci files.

MISSION FILE 3:3

Remember, a unicycle has 1 wheel, a bicycle has 2 wheels, a tricycle has 3 wheels and a quad bike has 4 wheels. It could be useful to draw quick sketches of the cycles on small pieces of paper. You can then try lots of different combinations to find all the possible answers to the problems. To help you find all the answers, only change 1 type of cycle at a time.

MISSION FILE 3:4

If you are drawing the rods, use a ruler (the rods must be straight) and make them fairly long to give you more space to work. Alternatively, use long strips of paper, flattened straws or moveable lines on a computer programme. You can arrange and rearrange these pieces of equipment without having to do lots of rubbing out! As you add each rod, always try to find the position where it will make the maximum number of intersections.

MISSION FILE 3:5

If all the agents have all the choices listed next to their names, you can use the clues to cross out choices that are not correct and circle the choices that are made by each agent. Remember that once you know a choice made by an agent, then none of the other agents can make the same choice, so it can be crossed off the list. You could put the information in a matrix and solve it that way.

MISSION FILE 3:6

It is easier to read and interpret data if it is in a sorting diagram, such as a Venn or Carroll diagram. Questions that don't use these will be easier if you use the data to create your own Venn or Carroll diagram. You can choose whichever you prefer – they work equally well. Most of the questions need 2 sets in the Venn diagram or 2 rows and 2 columns in the Carroll diagram, but watch out for those that need more!

For the second question in the Da Vinci files, you could start with 0 spaceships being cone shaped and having wings, and then work up 1 at a time.

MISSION FILE 3:7

In the Main Mission, look carefully at the outlines of the specimens and also at the shapes that they contain. Compare the ones that aren't Gruffles with the ones that are Gruffles. Can you spot what a Gruffle has to have to be a Gruffle and what the non-Gruffles have that stop them from being Gruffles?

Look at the Glimpians – are their edges curved or straight? What about the shapes inside them? Sometimes, knowing that something isn't what you want can help you to find out what you do want.

MISSION FILE 3:8

When you are finding different ways to fill a box with cubes, you might find it helpful to think about the number of cubes there can be in each layer. Each layer will have the same number of cubes and all the layers together should use the correct number of cubes to fill the box.

For example, if you are using 18 cubes to fill the box, you could have 6 in each layer as $6 + 6 + 6 = 18$. What other numbers could you have in each layer and still use 18 cubes altogether?

MISSION FILE 3:9

Some towns have enough roads to let you to get into the town on one road and get out again on a different road. It's very easy to pass through those towns. But some towns don't have enough roads to let you keep getting in on one road and out on another and they are the towns that might cause you more difficulty. You will need to think carefully about those towns!

If you can find out why you had trouble with Route 4 in the Training Mission, then you'll be able to help Echo sort out her route in Question 1 in the Main Mission.

The TASC Problem Solving Wheel

TASC: Thinking Actively in a Social Context

Learn from experience

Reflect
What have I learned?

Communicate

What have I learned?

Let's tell someone.

Communicate
Who can I tell?

TA

Evaluate

How well did I do?

Evaluate
Did I succeed? Can I think of another way?

Let's do it!

Implement
Now let me do it!

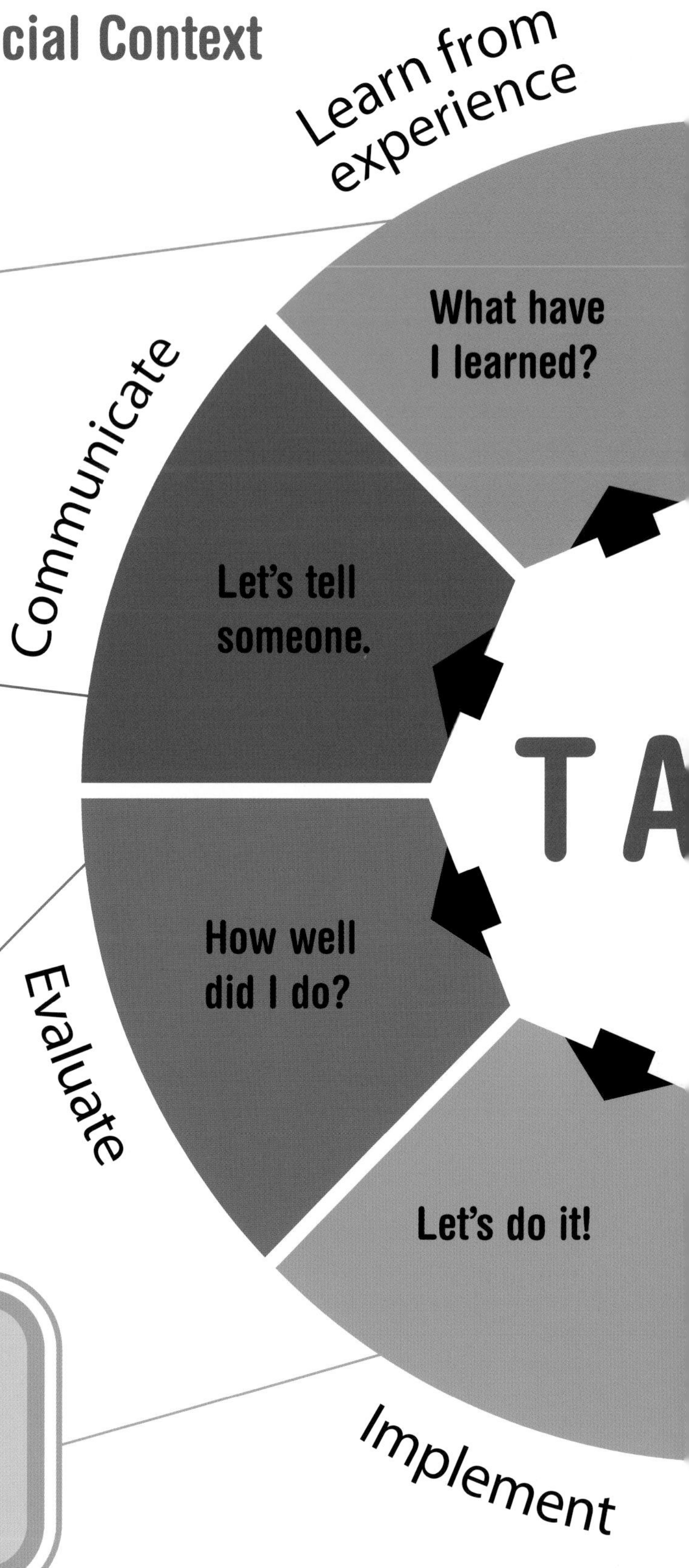

Implement

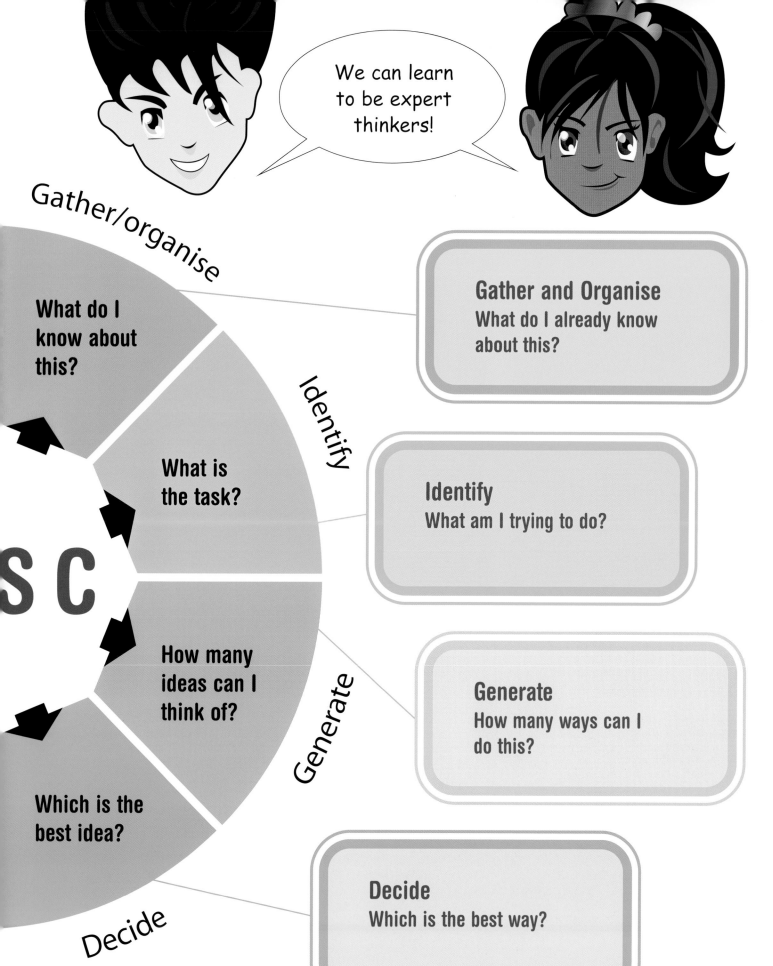

We can learn to be expert thinkers!

Gather/organise

What do I know about this?

What is the task?

How many ideas can I think of?

Which is the best idea?

T A S C

Identify

Generate

Decide

Gather and Organise
What do I already know about this?

Identify
What am I trying to do?

Generate
How many ways can I do this?

Decide
Which is the best way?

TASC: Thinking Actively in a Social Context © Belle Wallace 2004

47

nace

What is NACE?

NACE is a charity which was set up in 1984. It is an organisation that supports the teaching of 'more-able' pupils and helps all children find out what they are good at and to do their best.

What does NACE do?

NACE helps teachers by giving them advice, books, materials and training. Many teachers, headteachers, parents and governors join NACE. Members of NACE can use a special website which gives them useful advice, ideas and materials to help children to learn.

NACE helps thousands of schools and teachers every year. It also helps teachers and children in other countries, such as America and China.

How will this book help me?

Brain Academy Supermaths books challenge and help you to become better at learning and a better mathematician by:
- Thinking of and testing different solutions to problems
- Making connections to what you already know
- Making mistakes and learning from them
- Working with your teacher, by yourself and with others
- Expecting you to get better and to go on to the next book
- Learning skills which you can use in other subjects and out of school

We hope that you enjoy the books!

Write to **RISING STARS** and let us know how the books helped you to learn and what you would like to see in the next books.

Rising Stars UK Ltd, 22 Grafton Street, London W1S 4EX